Ears

Words to practise

ears   hear

clear   beard

too   meets

Ella the rabbit has ears that stick up.

'thump'

'thump'

'thump'

Ella can hear 'thump, thump, thump'.

Ella meets Fluff.

Fluff is a rabbit too.

Fluff has long ears that flop.

'Can you hear with
ears that flop?'

'thud'
'thud'
'thud'

'I can hear as clear as you.'
'Thud, thud, thud'.

'Thud' It is Dillon.

Oh! He has a beard!